Scottish Slimmers

seasons

First published in 2007 by Weight Management (UK) Ltd

www.scottishslimmers.com

© Weight Management (UK) Ltd 2007

Managing editor: Alexandra Howie
Nutrition: Tanya May

Designed and produced by SP Creative Design
Editor: Heather Thomas
Design and production: Rolando Ugolini
Photography: by Simon Smith
Food stylist: Mari Mererid Williams

Printed and bound by Everbest in China

Key to recipes

All values given in the recipes are for calories, Checks and grams of fat (in that order), excluding No-Check foods, and are **per serving** unless stated otherwise.

contents

spring

A week of main meals for spring

chunky minestrone

Prep: **15** minutes Cook: approx. **2** hours

Enjoy this filling soup for a healthy lunch, or serve it with crusty bread or a salad for your main evening meal. The quantities given make a big pot of soup but it will keep in the fridge for a few days, or you can freeze some for later use.

1 onion, chopped
2 sticks celery, chopped
2 carrots, chopped
2 leeks, chopped
1 garlic clove, crushed
1500 ml/2½ pints vegetable stock
4 large tomatoes, skinned and chopped
1 bay leaf
sprigs of fresh thyme
350 g/12 oz diced potato
1 x 200 g/7 oz can haricot beans, drained
225 g/8 oz spring greens, shredded
60 g/2 oz vermicelli or soup pasta
salt and ground black pepper

1 Put the onion, celery, carrots, leeks, garlic and vegetable stock in a large saucepan. Cover the pan and bring to the boil. Boil hard for 5 minutes, then uncover and simmer for about 30 minutes until the vegetables are tender.

2 Add the chopped tomatoes and herbs. Season with salt and pepper and simmer for about 1 hour.

3 Add the potato and haricot beans and continue cooking gently for 15 minutes, then stir in the spring greens and pasta. Cook for about 10 minutes until the pasta is cooked.

4 Check the seasoning and remove the bay leaf. Serve ladled into warm bowls.

grilled cod with lentils

Prep: **10** minutes Cook: **30** minutes

With the emphasis on healthy low-GI foods, lentils are a delicious accompaniment to grilled fish. They are also a good source of protein and fibre.

125 g/4½ oz green lentils, e.g. Le Puy
1 carrot, diced
1 celery stick, diced
1 garlic clove, crushed
1 bay leaf
juice of ½ lemon
1 tablespoon oil-free vinaigrette dressing
½ teaspoon Dijon mustard
few sprigs of parsley, chopped
2 x 175 g/6 oz skinless, boneless cod steaks or fillets
salt and ground black pepper

1 Rinse the lentils under running cold water, and then put them in a saucepan with the carrot, celery, garlic and bay leaf. Cover with cold water and bring to the boil.

2 Skim off any froth on the surface, then cover and simmer for about 20 minutes until tender.

3 Drain the lentils and then add the lemon juice, vinaigrette, mustard and parsley. Stir well and season to taste.

4 Meanwhile, grill the cod steaks under a hot overhead grill, or cook for 3–4 minutes each side in a ridged grill pan which has been sprayed with a little oil.

5 Divide the lentils between 2 serving plates and place a cod steak on top. Serve with fresh spring vegetables or a crisp salad.

spring cabbage parcels

SERVES **two** | 95 | **4** ③

Prep: **10** minutes Cook: **20** minutes

These steamed cabbage parcels are easy to cook, low in Checks and taste fabulous. If you are vegetarian, you could substitute Quorn mince for the pork in this recipe.

6 large spring green or dark green cabbage leaves
125 g/4½ oz minced pork (max. 5% fat)
1 tablespoon Thai green curry paste
2 spring onions, finely sliced
60 g/2 oz finely chopped mushrooms
60 g/2 oz bean sprouts
1 tablespoon chopped coriander
salt and ground black pepper

1 Add the spring green or cabbage leaves to a pan of boiling salted water. Blanch for 30 seconds, remove the leaves with a slotted spoon and refresh in cold water. Drain and pat dry.

2 Mix together the pork, curry paste, spring onions, mushrooms and bean sprouts. Stir in the coriander and seasoning.

3 Spread the cabbage leaves out and divide the filling between them. Roll each leaf around the filling, tucking in the sides and wrapping up to form a parcel. Secure with a cocktail stick.

4 Place the parcels in the top of a steamer or in a colander over a pan of simmering water. Cover and cook for 20 minutes, until the pork is cooked and the leaves are green and tender.

5 Serve with cooked noodles (100 cals, 4 Checks, 0.5 g fat for 30 g/1 oz dry weight or 75 g/2½ oz cooked weight) and sweet chilli sauce (30 cals, 1 Check, 0 g fat for 1 level dessertspoon).

spicy pasta supper with broccoli

SERVES **two** | 295 | **12** ⑧

Prep: **5** minutes Cook: **10–15** minutes

During March, purple sprouting broccoli is starting to come into season. If you cannot find any, use normal broccoli instead. Or add 100 g/3½ oz can tuna in brine with the chilli and anchovies. This will add 40 cals, 1.5 Checks, 0 g fat per serving.

125 g/4½ oz penne or pasta tubes
300 g/10 oz broccoli florets, preferably purple sprouting
spray oil
2 garlic cloves, sliced
¼ teaspoon dried chilli flakes
6 anchovy fillets, drained
1 tablespoon pine nuts
salt and ground black pepper
1 tablespoon chopped flat-leaf parsley

1 Cook the penne in a large pan of lightly salted boiling water according to the packet instructions until tender. Drain well.

2 Meanwhile, steam the broccoli florets until tender or cook in a pan of lightly salted boiling water. Drain well.

3 While the pasta and broccoli are cooking, lightly spray a non-stick pan with oil and cook the garlic over a low heat until soft. Add the chilli flakes and anchovies and cook for 1–2 minutes. Stir in the pine nuts and season to taste.

4 Tip the cooked pasta and broccoli into the pan and gently toss together. Sprinkle with parsley and serve immediately.

pot roasted chicken with leeks

Prep: **10** minutes Cook: **1** hour **20** minutes

1 red onion, peeled and cut into wedges

2 leeks, trimmed and thickly sliced

2 celery sticks, sliced

2 carrots, sliced

2 garlic cloves, crushed

4 tomatoes, skinned and chopped

1 x 1.5 kg/3 lb chicken, preferably free-range

150 ml/¼ pint unsweetened apple juice

150 ml/¼ pint dry cider

salt and ground black pepper

chopped parsley, to serve

1 Put the red onion, leeks, celery, carrots, garlic and tomatoes in a flameproof casserole dish which is large enough to take the chicken.

2 Wash the chicken under running cold water and pat dry. Remove any fat remaining inside and peel away and discard as much skin as possible.

3 Season the chicken with salt and pepper, and then push it, breast-side down, into the vegetables.

4 Pour the apple juice and cider over the top and cover the casserole with a lid. Place it over a high heat and, when the juices start to boil, reduce the heat to a simmer and cook gently for 30 minutes.

5 Now turn the chicken over, breast-side up, then cover the casserole and cook gently for about 50 minutes. You can test whether the chicken is cooked by inserting a skewer or knife behind the thigh – if the juices, run clear, it is ready. If not, cook for a little longer.

6 Remove the chicken and carve into serving pieces, removing any skin. Arrange on serving plates with the vegetables and juices. Sprinkle with chopped parsley and serve with some boiled rice (100 cals, 4 Checks, 0.5 g fat for each 30 g/1 oz dry weight or 75 g/2½ oz cooked weight).

A pot roast is warming and nourishing on a chilly, bright spring day. And because everything cooks in the same pan, there is less washing up afterwards!

orange and lemon cheesecake

SERVES eight

Prep: **20** minutes Cook: **10** minutes Chill: **2–3** hours

Oranges and lemons are still sweet and juicy at this time of year, and the large Navel oranges are especially good. Cheer yourself up on a cold day with a slice of this delicious creamy cheesecake.

115 g/4 oz ginger thin biscuits
40 g/1½ oz melted butter
grated zest and juice of 1 large lemon
1 sachet powdered gelatine
200 g/7 oz 0% fat Greek yoghurt
500 g/17 oz Quark
60 g/2 oz caster sugar
2 large egg yolks
grated zest and juice of 1 orange
1 teaspoon icing sugar, for dusting
shredded zest of 1 orange and 1 lemon, for decoration

1 Crush the ginger thins with a rolling pin or whizz in a food processor. Mix them into the melted butter and then press down firmly into the base of a loose-based, deep 20 cm/8 in cake tin. Bake in a preheated oven at 170°C, 325°F, Gas Mark 3 for 10 minutes. Remove and cool.

2 Put the lemon juice in a heatproof basin, sprinkle with the gelatine and leave for 5 minutes. Suspend the basin over a pan of simmering water until the gelatine completely dissolves.

3 In a blender or food processor, blend the Greek yoghurt, Quark, sugar, egg yolks, grated lemon zest, orange zest and juice. Strain in the gelatine liquid and quickly blend until thoroughly mixed.

4 Spoon the mixture into the cake tin over the ginger thin base and chill in the refrigerator for 2–3 hours until firm and set.

5 To serve the cheesecake, remove it from the tin and dust lightly with icing sugar. Sprinkle the shredded zest over the top and cut into slices.

ice cream with pink rhubarb

SERVES two

Prep: **5** minutes Cook: **10** minutes

Rhubarb is still in season and you may well have a crown in your garden. Use it up now while the stalks are still really pink and before they go green and stringy.

225 g/8 oz trimmed rhubarb stalks
grated zest and juice of 1 orange
1 teaspoon grated fresh root ginger
1 tablespoon caster sugar
2 scoops low-fat vanilla ice cream

1 Cut the rhubarb into 2cm/1in chunks and then place in a saucepan with the orange zest and juice, ginger, caster sugar and 2 tablespoons water.

2 Over a low heat, stir the sugar into the juice until dissolved and cook gently until the rhubarb is tender but not mushy. It should retain its shape.

3 Remove the rhubarb with a slotted spoon and boil any pan juices to reduce to a syrup. Serve hot or cold with a scoop of ice cream, with the juices poured over the top.

smoked salmon and dill crêpes

SERVES **two** 325 **13** ⑪

Prep: **10** minutes Stand: **10** minutes Cook: **10** minutes

These savoury crêpes will make a light but delicious supper. You can make the batter in advance and leave it to stand until required. Serve with a salad of rocket, baby spinach leaves or watercress.

60 g/2 oz plain flour
pinch of salt
1 medium egg
150 ml/¼ pint skimmed milk
spray olive oil
4 tablespoons half-fat crème fraîche
150 g/5 oz smoked salmon pieces
2 tablespoons chopped dill
freshly ground black pepper
1 lemon, quartered

1 Make the batter: sift the flour and salt into a bowl and whisk in the egg and milk until smooth and free from lumps. Allow to stand for at least 10 minutes.

2 Lightly spray a non-stick frying pan with oil and place over a medium heat. When it's really hot, pour in half of the batter and tilt the pan so that it covers the base evenly. When it is set and golden underneath, flip the crêpe over and cook the other side. Remove and keep warm while you cook the other crêpe.

3 Divide the crème fraîche between the crêpes and sprinkle with the salmon, dill and black pepper. Fold over and serve immediately with salad.

Boursin stuffed chicken

SERVES **two** 270 **11** ⑨

Prep: **5** minutes Cook: **30** minutes

Chicken breasts take on a new dimension when they are filled with Boursin Light and served with baby spring vegetables in a creamy sauce.

2 x 150 g/5 oz boned, skinless chicken breasts
60 g/2 oz Boursin Light
spray oil
2 small leeks, finely sliced
60 ml/2 fl oz Noilly Prat or dry white vermouth or white wine
4 tablespoons half-fat crème fraîche
salt and ground black pepper
snipped chives

1 Make a slit in each chicken breast and fill with the Boursin Light. Secure with cocktail sticks.

2 Spray a frying pan lightly with spray oil and sear the chicken breasts on both sides over a high heat for 1–2 minutes.

3 Place the chicken breasts in an ovenproof dish and bake in a preheated oven at 180°C, 350°F, Gas Mark 4 for 30 minutes, or until cooked through.

4 Add the leeks to the oil left in the pan and cook gently over a low heat until tender. Add the Noilly Prat and bring to the boil. When it evaporates, reduce the heat and stir in the crème fraîche. Heat through gently for 2 minutes and season to taste.

5 Pour the sauce around the chicken breasts and sprinkle with the chives. Serve with steamed baby carrots, courgettes, thin green beans or mange-tout.

Thai seafood curry

SERVES **two** | 250 | 10 | 13

Prep: **5** minutes   Cook: **10** minutes

This quick Thai-style curry is so simple to make. You can use a pack of fresh mixed seafood from the chilled fish section in your supermarket or just defrost a bag of mixed frozen seafood.

100 g/3½ oz thin green beans, trimmed

100 g/3½ oz fresh peas or mange-tout

200 ml/7 fl oz reduced-fat coconut milk

1 tablespoon Thai green curry paste

200 g/7 oz mixed seafood (e.g. prawns, squid, mussels, scallops)

3 tablespoons chopped fresh coriander

lemon or lime wedges, to serve

1 Steam the green beans and peas or mange-tout until just tender, or cook them in a pan of boiling water. Drain well.

2 Put the coconut milk and curry paste in a wok or deep frying pan. Stir well and heat through gently. Add the mixed seafood and cook gently for about 3–4 minutes until cooked.

3 Stir in the drained vegetables and chopped coriander, and check the seasoning.

4 Serve with lemon or lime wedges and some plain boiled rice (100 cals, 4 Checks, 0.5 g fat for each 30 g/1 oz dry weight or 75 g/2½ oz cooked weight).

spring lamb with rosemary

SERVES **four** | 160 | 6 | 7

Prep: **15** minutes   Cook: **1** hour

Ready-prepared boneless legs of lamb are now available in most supermarkets. Alternatively, ask your butcher to do this for you. Choose a lean joint with minimal fat. Removing the bone makes the lamb easier to carve, but remember to cut off any visible fat from the cooked joint before eating.

1 x 400 g/14 oz boned and rolled leg of lamb

1 bulb garlic, separated into peeled cloves

few sprigs of fresh rosemary

salt and ground black pepper

spray oil

Mint sauce:

60 ml/2 fl oz wine vinegar

1 teaspoon caster sugar

1 bunch fresh mint, finely chopped

1 Using a sharp knife, make many incisions all over the top of the lamb joint. Slice the garlic cloves and insert the slivers of garlic into the incisions, pushing them in well. Cut the rosemary into smaller sprigs and push them into the incisions, too.

2 Spray lightly with oil and season with salt and pepper. Place the lamb in a roasting pan and cook in a preheated oven at 180°C, 350°F, Gas Mark 4 for 1 hour, or until it is cooked to your liking. It may need a little longer if you prefer it well done.

3 When cooked, remove from the oven and transfer the joint to a carving board. Cover with foil and leave to rest for 10 minutes.

4 To make the mint sauce, blend the wine vinegar and sugar. Stir the chopped mint into the sauce with a pinch of salt.

5 Carve the lamb thinly, removing any visible fat. Serve with green vegetables, carrots, new potatoes (70 cals, 3 Checks per 100 g/3½ oz) and gravy made with low-fat gravy granules.

SERVES four | 80 **3** **①** warm new potato salad

Prep: **15** minutes Cook: **8–10** minutes

The first new potatoes are now appearing in the shops and it's time to indulge yourself without worrying about your waistline. If you can get them, the Jersey Royals are the sweetest and most flavoursome.

- 400 g/14 oz small new potatoes
- 1 bunch spring onions, trimmed and finely chopped
- 4–5 tablespoons chopped parsley
- few sprigs of mint, chopped
- small bundle of chives, snipped
- 75 ml/2½ fl oz fat-free vinaigrette dressing
- 1 teaspoon honey mustard or Dijon mustard
- juice of 1 small lemon
- salt and ground black pepper

1 Scrub the new potatoes and cut them in half. Cook in salted boiling water for 8–10 minutes until tender. Drain well.

2 Tip the hot potatoes into a large serving bowl and add the spring onions and chopped herbs.

3 Blend the vinaigrette with the honey mustard and lemon juice and season to taste. Toss the hot potatoes with the dressing. Grind some black pepper over the top, adding a little sea salt if wished, and serve warm.

OR...

To make this more substantial, add 100 g/3½ oz cooked diced lean bacon or ham (45 cals, 2 Checks, 1.5 g fat per serving).

SERVES two | 210 **8** **③** Japanese chicken noodle soup

Prep: **10** minutes Cook: **10** minutes

For the best flavour, try to use home-made chicken stock or a tub of fresh stock. You can now buy sachets of Japanese miso paste in most supermarkets or oriental stores.

- 300 ml/½ pint fresh chicken stock
- 200 ml/7 fl oz boiling water
- 1 sachet Japanese miso paste (or 1 tablespoon yellow miso paste)
- small knob fresh root ginger, peeled and thinly sliced
- 1 lemon grass stalk, finely sliced
- 1 small carrot, cut into thin strips
- 4 spring onions, shredded
- 175 g/6 oz skinless chicken breast fillets, thinly sliced
- 2 pak choi, shredded
- 150 g/5 oz fresh 'straight-to-wok' noodles

1 Put the stock, boiling water, miso paste, ginger and lemon grass in a pan and bring to the boil. Simmer for 2 minutes.

2 Add the carrot and spring onions, and simmer for 3 minutes. Add the chicken and pak choi and simmer for 3 minutes.

3 Meanwhile, drop the noodles into a pan of boiling water and cook for about 2 minutes until tender. Drain and add to the soup. Serve immediately.

OR...

To ring the changes with this clear, refreshing soup, you can add spinach, some sliced mushrooms or garlic. Season with a few shakes of Thai fish sauce.

Maryland crabcakes

SERVES **two** 190 **8** **6**

Prep: **15** minutes Chill: **1** hour Cook: **8** minutes

1 small egg, beaten
1 tablespoon low-calorie mayonnaise
¼ teaspoon Dijon mustard
grated zest and juice of ½ lemon
2 tablespoons chopped parsley
300 g/10 oz white crab meat
salt and ground black pepper
flour for dusting
spray oil

Balsamic tomato salad:
2 large tomatoes, thinly sliced
½ small red onion, finely chopped
few basil leaves, torn into strips
1 teaspoon balsamic vinegar

1 Mix together the beaten egg, mayonnaise and mustard until well blended. Add the lemon zest and juice, and then stir in the herbs and crab meat. Season with salt and pepper.

2 Shape the mixture into 4 patties, wrap in clingfilm and chill in the refrigerator for at least 1 hour to firm them up.

3 Dust the patties lightly with flour. Cook them in a hot non-stick frying pan., which has been sprayed lightly with oil, for about 4 minutes on both sides until golden brown and crisp.

4 Meanwhile, arrange the sliced tomatoes, onion and basil on 2 serving plates. Season to taste and drizzle with balsamic vinegar. Serve with the hot crabcakes, with a little sweet chilli dipping sauce, if wished.

These American-style crabcakes are best made with fresh seasonal crabs, but if you can't find any, you can cheat and use some canned or frozen crab meat instead.

mussels with tomatoes and pesto

SERVES **two** 240 **10** **11**
SERVES **four** 120 **5** **6**

Prep: **15** minutes Cook: **10** minutes

1 kg/2 lb fresh mussels in their shells
1 teaspoon olive oil
1 small onion, finely chopped
100 ml/3½ fl oz red wine
1 x 400 g/14 oz can chopped tomatoes
1 tablespoon green pesto
salt and ground black pepper
3 tablespoons chopped parsley

1 Put the mussels in the sink or a large bowl of cold water. Discard any that are open, damaged or cracked. Scrub the remaining mussels well, removing the 'beards' with a sharp knife.

2 Heat the oil in a large saucepan and cook the onion over a low heat until soft. Add the red wine and cook for 2 minutes, then stir in the tomatoes and 100 ml/3½ fl oz boiling water. Bring to the boil.

3 Add the mussels, cover the pan and cook over a high heat, shaking the pan occasionally, for about 5 minutes, or until the mussels open. Discard any that fail to open.

4 Stir in the pesto and season to taste with salt and pepper. Serve immediately sprinkled with parsley.

If you thought mussels are too complicated to cook, think again. Easy to prepare, they cook in minutes and have the bonus of being low in calories. This recipe serves two as a main course, or four as a starter.

gammon and potato cake stack

SERVES two | 340 | 14 | ⑫

Prep: **10** minutes Cook: **30** minutes

Here's a different way of serving a gammon steak – more like an all-day breakfast!

250 g/9 oz potatoes, peeled and cut into chunks
150 g/5 oz baby spinach
1 tablespoon half-fat crème fraîche
4 spring onions, finely chopped
spray oil
2 x 125 g/4½ oz lean gammon steaks, fat removed
2 medium eggs
salt and ground black pepper

1 Cook the potatoes in a large pan of salted water for about 15 minutes, until cooked but not mushy. Drain well.

2 Put the spinach in a colander and pour boiling water over it. Press down with a saucepan to squeeze out any liquid, then chop.

3 Mash the potato with the crème fraîche; stir in the spinach and spring onions. Season and shape into 2 round patties. Cook the potato cakes in a hot pan sprayed with oil for about 5 minutes each side. When golden, remove and keep warm.

4 Meanwhile, grill the gammon steaks for about 4–5 minutes each side until cooked.

5 Poach the eggs in an egg poacher, or break them into a pan of simmering water and cook until the whites are set.

6 Place a gammon steak on top of each potato cake and top with a poached egg. Serve with green vegetables or a salad.

lamb burgers with tzatziki

SERVES two | 200 | 8 | ⑬

Prep: **15** minutes Chill: **30** minutes Cook: **8–10** minutes

Lamb can be quite high in fat, so it's best to buy some really lean fillet or leg steaks and then mince the meat yourself in a mincer or whizz until ground up in a food processor.

225 g/8 oz lean minced lamb
2 garlic cloves, crushed
½ small onion, grated
3 tablespoons chopped fresh mint
3–4 drops Worcestershire sauce
salt and ground black pepper
spray oil

Tzatziki:
100 g/3½ oz 0% fat Greek yoghurt
¼ cucumber, diced
1 garlic clove, crushed
2 tablespoons finely chopped mint
2 tablespoons chopped parsley

1 Mix together the minced lamb, garlic, onion and mint. Add the Worcestershire sauce and seasoning. Divide the mixture into 2 equal parts and mould each one into a burger. Chill in the refrigerator for 30 minutes.

2 Meanwhile, mix all the tzatziki ingredients together and place in the refrigerator until needed.

3 Spray a griddle pan lightly with oil and place over a medium heat. When it's hot, add the burgers and cook for 4–5 minutes each side, depending on how well cooked you like your lamb.

4 Serve the burgers hot with the tzatziki and a mixed salad or some griddled vegetables.

courgette frittata with tomato sauce

SERVES **two** 190 8 14

Prep: **5** minutes   Cook: **20** minutes

A frittata is an Italian omelette, but it's much more chunky and filling than our usual familiar ones, so you can cut it into wedges and eat it hot or cold.

1 onion, chopped
2 garlic cloves, crushed
spray oil
3 small courgettes, sliced
4 medium eggs
small bunch of chives, snipped
1 tablespoon grated Parmesan cheese
150 g/5 oz cherry tomatoes
shredded basil leaves
salt and ground black pepper

1 Cook the onion and garlic until softened in a small frying pan or large omelette pan which has been sprayed with oil. Add the courgettes and cook over a medium heat until golden and tender.

2 Beat the eggs with the chives, season with salt and pepper, and tip in the courgette mixture. Mix well.

3 Pour the egg and courgette mixture back into the pan and cook over a very low heat for about 10 minutes, until the omelette is set and golden underneath.

4 Sprinkle with Parmesan and pop the pan under a hot grill. Cook for about 3 minutes until golden and set on top.

5 Meanwhile, heat a pan sprayed lightly with oil and cook the cherry tomatoes, pressing them slightly with a spoon, until tender and juicy. Season and sprinkle with basil. Serve the frittata cut into wedges with the warm cherry tomato sauce.

gooseberry and elderflower fool

SERVES **six** 80 3 0

Prep: **10** minutes   Cook: **10** minutes   Chill: **1** hour

If you are fortunate enough to have some elderflowers in bloom in your garden or hedgerows, you can tie some flowers in a piece of muslin and suspend it in the gooseberries while they are cooking for a heavenly scent and flavour.

450 g/1 lb gooseberries
45 g/1½ oz caster sugar
2 teaspoons elderflower cordial
300 ml/½ pint 0% fat plain Greek yoghurt

1 Top and tail the gooseberries, snipping off the ends. Place them in a saucepan with the sugar and elderflower cordial. Stir and cook very gently over a low heat for 10 minutes, until the gooseberries soften and start to look yellow.

2 Crush the cooked gooseberries with a wooden spoon and allow to cool. Gently swirl in the Greek yoghurt and transfer to a serving bowl. Chill in the refrigerator before serving.

OR...

You can make a fool with any crushed soft fruit. Why not try strawberries, raspberries or redcurrants?

summer

A week of main meals for summer:

spinach and ricotta filo parcels

SERVES **four** 130 5 7

Prep: **20** minutes Cook: **15–20** minutes

These delicious veggie parcels make a light starter for a summer dinner party or elegant party snacks. They do not take long to make and look fabulous.

450 g/1 lb baby spinach leaves
125 g/4½ oz ricotta cheese
good pinch of freshly grated nutmeg
1 egg yolk, beaten
4 x 15 g/½ oz sheets filo pastry
1 large egg, beaten
salt and pepper

1 Put the spinach in a pan with 1 tablespoon water. Cover and cook gently over a low heat for 4–5 minutes, shaking the pan occasionally, until the leaves are bright green. Drain in a colander, pressing down with a saucer to squeeze out any juice. Chop the spinach and mix in a bowl with the ricotta, nutmeg, beaten egg yolk and seasoning.

2 Brush a filo pastry sheet with beaten egg and cut into 3 long strips. Fold each strip over lengthways and place a small spoonful of the ricotta mixture at one end. Fold the pastry over to make a triangle, then fold again in the same way. Continue folding until the strip is used up and you have a thick triangle.

3 Brush with beaten egg and place on a greased baking sheet. Make the other pastries in the same way. Cook in a preheated oven at 190°C, 375°F, Gas Mark 5 for 15–20 minutes until crisp.

salmon with herb mayonnaise

SERVES **two** 310 12 19

Prep: **10** minutes Cook: **20** minutes

Salmon served with a classic mayonnaise is the perfect dish for a hot summer's day. You can cook the salmon in advance, if wished, and then serve it cold later. If you can get hold of any salmon trout (in season in June), its fine flavour and delicate texture are even better.

2 x 150 g/5 oz salmon fillets
few sprigs of tarragon and dill
juice of ½ lemon
salt and ground black pepper

Herb mayonnaise:
½ bunch fresh watercress
85 g/3 oz virtually fat-free fromage frais
2 tablespoons low-calorie mayonnaise
1 tablespoon chopped fresh tarragon
1 teaspoon capers
squeeze of lemon juice

1 Place the salmon on a sheet of kitchen foil with the herbs. Sprinkle with lemon juice and seasoning. Fold the foil over the salmon to make a sealed parcel. Place on a baking tray.

2 Cook in a medium oven at 180°C, 350°F, Gas Mark 4 for about 20 minutes, until the salmon is cooked through.

3 Make the herb mayonnaise. Boil the watercress in a pan of boiling water for 30 seconds. Drain well, squeeze dry and chop.

4 Mix together the fromage frais, mayonnaise, tarragon and capers. Stir in the watercress and lemon juice. Season to taste.

5 Serve the salmon hot or cold with the mayonnaise and some new potatoes (70 cals, 3 Checks per 100 g/3½ oz).

chicken with pesto noodles

SERVES **two** | 410 | **16** ⑩

Prep: **10** minutes Cook: **20–30** minutes

2 x 150 g/5 oz skinless, boneless chicken breasts

spray oil

1 red onion, peeled and cut into wedges

1 red pepper, de-seeded and cut into strips

115 g/4 oz fresh egg noodles

1 tablespoon green pesto

salt and ground black pepper

1 Cook the chicken breasts in a lightly oiled ridged griddle pan for about 10–15 minutes each side, until thoroughly cooked through and golden brown.

2 After about 15 minutes, add the red onion and pepper strips to the chicken in the pan. Cook, turning occasionally, until they are tender but not too charred.

3 Cook the fresh egg noodles, according to the instructions on the pack. Drain thoroughly and toss with the pesto.

4 Spoon the pesto noodles on to 2 serving plates. Place a chicken breast and some griddled vegetables on top and serve immediately with a crisp salad.

This makes a quick and easy supper dish when you are in a hurry. If wished, you can use red pesto instead of green.

Greek stuffed tomatoes

SERVES **two** | 110 | **4** ①

Prep: **15** minutes Cook: **1** hour

4 very large ripe tomatoes

½ onion, finely chopped

1 garlic clove, crushed

spray oil

1 small courgette, diced

2 spring onions, finely chopped

4 black olives, pitted and chopped

3–4 tablespoons chopped parsley

60 g/2 oz long-grain rice, rinsed

salt and freshly ground black pepper

1 Slice the top thinly off each tomato and reserve for a 'lid'. Scoop out the flesh and seeds to leave an outer shell for stuffing. Finely chop the flesh and place in a bowl.

2 Cook the rice according to the instructions on the pack. Drain thoroughly.

3 Cook the onion and garlic gently in a pan sprayed with oil until softened. Add the courgette and cook until soft. Mix with the tomato flesh, spring onions, olives and herbs. Stir in the rice and season with salt and pepper.

4 Fill the tomato shells with the rice and vegetable mixture. Cover with the reserved 'lids' and place in a baking dish. Cook in a preheated oven at 190°C, 375°F, Gas Mark 5 for 1 hour. Eat hot or cold.

You will need to buy the large slicing tomatoes to make this dish. If you can get them, the Marmande variety has the best flavour.

Spanish summer vegetable tortilla

SERVES **two** | 290 | **12** | ⑮

Prep: **15** minutes Cook: **30** minutes

This tortilla is equally good served hot or cold. Cut into wedges, it makes the perfect food for your packed lunches and picnics.

300 g/10 oz potatoes, peeled and diced
spray oil
2 garlic cloves, thinly sliced
1 red pepper
1 yellow pepper
4 large eggs
1 tablespoon chopped parsley
salt and ground black pepper

1 Cook the potatoes in a hot frying pan lightly sprayed with oil. Turn them occasionally and, after 5 minutes, add the garlic. Continue cooking until they are tender and golden.

2 Meanwhile, place the peppers under a hot grill and cook, turning occasionally, until the skins are charred. Peel away the skins and remove the seeds. Cut the pepper flesh into thin slices.

3 Beat the eggs, stir in the chopped parsley and season with salt and pepper. Stir in the cooked potatoes and peppers. Pour the omelette mixture into the frying pan and cook gently for 15 minutes, until set around the sides and underneath.

4 Pop the pan under a preheated grill for 2–3 minutes until the omelette is set and golden brown. Serve cut into wedges.

tabbouleh with grilled spiced beef

SERVES **two** | 285 | **11** | ⑧

Prep: **30** minutes Marinate: **12** hours Cook: **12** minutes

This is a special occasion dish as beef fillet is very expensive. However, you can buy lean sirloin or rump steak and spice it in the same way.

225 g/8 oz beef fillet, fat removed
2 tablespoons soy sauce
pinch of ground star anise
1 garlic clove, crushed
1 bird's eye chilli, finely chopped
1 teaspoon finely chopped ginger
spray oil

Tabbouleh:
75 g/2½ oz bulgur wheat
¼ cucumber, diced
2 ripe tomatoes, diced
3 spring onions, finely sliced
2 tablespoons chopped parsley
2 tablespoons chopped mint
juice of 1 lemon
2 tablespoons oil-free dressing

1 Put the beef fillet in a bowl. Mix together the soy sauce, star anise, garlic, chilli and ginger, and pour over the beef. Season generously with salt and pepper, cover and marinate in the refrigerator for at least 12 hours.

2 Make the tabbouleh: pour enough boiling water over the bulgur wheat to cover it and then soak for about 15 minutes. Squeeze out any excess moisture, and mix in the remaining ingredients, and stir well.

3 Heat a griddle pan which has been sprayed lightly with oil. Lift the beef out of the marinade and cook over a high heat for about 5–6 minutes each side, until cooked to your liking.

4 Carve the beef into thin slices and serve with the tabbouleh and some crisp lettuce or green beans.

MAKES
12 | **120 5 6** summer berry shortcakes

Prep: **20** minutes Chill: **30** minutes Cook: **6–8** minutes

You can use a variety of summer fruits to top these little shortcakes, depending on what is in season. Strawberries, raspberries, peaches or redcurrants all work well in this recipe.

85 g/3 oz butter
3 tablespoons caster sugar
115 g/4 oz plain flour, sifted
pinch of salt
150 g/5 oz very low-fat thick strawberry or raspberry yoghurt
175 g/6 oz strawberries, sliced
sprigs of mint, to decorate

1 Cream the butter and sugar together, either with an electric whisk or a food processor. Add the sifted flour and salt and mix to a stiff dough.

2 Knead lightly, then wrap the dough in some clingfilm and refrigerate for about 30 minutes.

3 On a lightly floured surface, roll out the dough 5mm/¼in thick. Cut out 12 x 5cm/2in circles and use to line a tartlet or muffin tin. Prick the bases.

4 Bake the shortcakes in a preheated oven at 170°C, 325°F, Gas Mark 3 for 6–8 minutes, until cooked. Remove and cool them on a wire rack.

5 Stir most of the sliced strawberries into the yoghurt, and use this mixture to fill the cooled shortcake tartlets. Decorate with the remaining strawberries and mint sprigs.

OR...

Instead of using fruit yoghurt, substitute the same quantity of virtually fat-free fromage frais and mix with the fresh fruit. You can also make these tartlets at other times of year, filled with blackberries, blueberries or even chopped citrus fruit.

Spanish chilled soup

SERVES four No -Check

Prep: **15** minutes Chill: **2–3** hours

When the weather is swelteringly hot, this soup will cool you down. It is based on the traditional gazpacho which is served at restaurants all over Spain during the summer.

450 g/1 lb ripe tomatoes, skinned and chopped

1 red pepper, de-seeded and chopped

1 green pepper, de-seeded and chopped

2 spring onions, chopped

½ cucumber, chopped

2 garlic cloves, crushed

2 tablespoons red wine vinegar

150 ml/¼ pint passata (sieved tomatoes)

300 ml/½ pint water

salt and ground black pepper

few drops of Tabasco (optional)

ice cubes

1 Put the tomatoes, peppers, spring onions, cucumber, garlic and wine vinegar in a food processor or large blender. With the lid held down firmly, blend until thoroughly puréed.

2 Pour into a large bowl and stir in the passata and water. Season to taste and add a shake of Tabasco, if wished. Chill in the refrigerator for several hours.

3 Serve chilled in bowls with added ice cubes. If wished, top with a garnish of diced peppers, red onion, cucumber and coriander.

quick mediterranean tart

SERVES four 210 **8** **8**

Prep: **15** minutes Cook: **20** minutes

This is a lovely tart for serving with a crisp salad on a hot day in summer. You can vary the vegetables used according to what is available.

8 x 15 g/½ oz sheets filo pastry

1 egg, beaten

2 tablespoons green pesto

1 red onion, thinly sliced

2 small courgettes, thinly sliced

1 red pepper, de-seeded and thinly sliced

225 g/8 oz cherry tomatoes

60 g/2 oz reduced-fat Cheddar cheese, grated

salt and ground black pepper

2–3 tablespoons chopped parsley

1 Lightly spray a 20 x 30cm (8 x 12in) shallow baking tin with oil. Brush a sheet of filo pastry with a little beaten egg and place in the tin with the edges hanging over the sides slightly. Repeat with the remaining sheets of pastry until the tin is lined and you have a filo shell.

2 Brush the pesto over the pastry base. Scatter the vegetables over the top, season and sprinkle with grated cheese.

3 Bake in a preheated oven at 190°C, 375°F, Gas Mark 5 for 20 minutes, until the pastry is crisp and golden, the vegetables are tender and the cheese has melted. Sprinkle with parsley and cut into quarters to serve.

SERVES two | 320 13 7 pasta with spiced crab and lemon

Prep: **5** minutes Cook: **10** minutes

Fresh crabs are usually plentiful in summer, and a little goes a long way. You can buy cooked dressed crabs from good fishmongers and supermarkets' fresh fish counters.

115 g/4 oz tagliatelle or fettuccine
1 teaspoon olive oil
3 garlic cloves, crushed
1 small red chilli, finely chopped
60 ml/2 fl oz white wine
juice of 1 lemon
1 x 125 g/4½ oz cooked dressed crab
1 bunch fresh parsley, chopped
salt and ground black pepper

1 Cook the pasta in a large pan of boiling salted water according to the packet directions, until it is just tender but still retains some bite. Drain well.

2 While the pasta is cooking, heat the olive oil in a large frying pan and cook the garlic and chilli for 1–2 minutes. Add the white wine and lemon juice, and gently cook for a few minutes to release the flavour and aroma.

3 Stir in the crab meat and chopped parsley and season to taste with salt and pepper. Heat through and toss with the cooked pasta until it is well coated. Serve immediately with watercress or rocket salad.

SERVES two | 180 7 4 summer chicken with minted peas

Prep: **10** minutes Cook: **35** minutes

Here's a classic summer chicken dish, featuring fresh garden peas in a creamy mint flavoured sauce. It is very easy to make but elegant enough for a dinner party.

1 small onion, finely chopped
1 garlic clove, crushed
spray oil
2 x 115 g/4 oz skinless, boneless chicken breasts
2 tablespoons dry white vermouth or wine
150 ml/¼ pint hot chicken stock
85 g/3 oz fresh shelled peas
2 tablespoons half-fat crème fraîche
small bunch of mint, finely chopped
salt and ground black pepper

1 Cook the onion and garlic for 2–3 minutes in a frying pan sprayed with oil. Add the chicken breasts and cook for about 4 minutes each side, or until golden.

2 Pour in the vermouth or white wine and let it bubble a little, then add the hot stock and cook over a low heat for about 10 minutes, turning the chicken halfway through.

3 Add the peas and simmer for 5 minutes until tender. When the chicken is cooked through, stir in the crème fraîche and mint. Simmer gently for 2–3 minutes and season to taste.

4 Serve hot with baby new potatoes (70 cals, 3 Checks per 100 g/3½ oz) and seasonal green vegetables or baby carrots.

lamb with Greek salad

SERVES **two** | 240 **10** ⑫

Prep: **15** minutes Marinate: **30** minutes Cook: **10** minutes

2 x 115 g/4 oz lean lamb leg steaks, all visible fat removed

2 garlic cloves, crushed

1 tablespoon chopped oregano and rosemary

juice of 1 lemon

salt and ground black pepper

Greek salad:

¼ cucumber, diced

2 ripe tomatoes, diced

4 spring onions, chopped

a few radishes, thickly sliced

85 g/3 oz reduced-fat feta cheese, diced

6 black olives

4 tablespoons chopped mint and parsley

2–3 tablespoons oil-free vinaigrette dressing

1 Place the lamb steaks in a shallow dish. Sprinkle with the garlic, oregano, rosemary and lemon juice, and season lightly with salt and pepper. Cover and leave to marinate in a cool place for 30 minutes.

2 When you are ready to cook the lamb, start preparing the Greek salad. Mix together the cucumber, tomatoes, spring onions, radishes, feta cheese and olives in a bowl. Scatter with the chopped herbs and set aside.

3 Cook the lamb steaks under a preheated hot grill for about 5 minutes each side, or cook in an oiled ridged grill pan or over hot coals on a barbecue.

4 Toss the salad in the dressing and add a good grinding of black pepper. Serve immediately with the hot lamb steaks.

OR...

This salad goes particularly well with barbecued kebabs, chicken, low-fat sausages and any kind of grilled fish. If you are vegetarian, try eating it with skewered vegetables (peppers, cherry tomatoes, mushrooms, courgettes) and halloumi cheese – delicious!

Lamb leg steaks are less fatty than chops; and there's also less wastage. If wished, you can prepare them in advance and marinate them overnight. This recipe will bring back memories of hot starlit nights sitting in Greek waterside tavernas!

seafood paella

SERVES **four** | 290 **8** ③

Prep: **10** minutes Cook: **40** minutes

You don't have to go to Spain on holiday – you can enjoy the authentic flavours at home with this colourful paella. It's perfect for al fresco entertaining.

1 large onion, chopped
2 garlic cloves, crushed
spray oil
1 red and 1 yellow pepper, de-seeded and sliced
225 g/8 oz Arborio or risotto rice
600 ml/1 pint fish stock
few strands of saffron
225 g/8 oz ripe tomatoes, skinned and chopped
350 g/12 oz mixed fresh seafood (or frozen, defrosted)
75 g/2½ oz fresh or frozen peas
salt and ground black pepper
2 tablespoons chopped parsley

1 In a very large deep frying pan, cook the onion and garlic in spray oil over a low heat until softened. Add the peppers and cook for about 3 minutes until tender.

2 Stir in the rice and cook for about 1 minute before adding some of the stock and saffron. Bring to the boil, then reduce the heat and add the tomatoes.

3 Cook gently, adding more stock as and when necessary, for about 20 minutes. When all the liquid has been absorbed and the rice is tender, add the seafood and peas. Season well with salt and pepper and cook for about 10 minutes. if the paella starts to stick to the pan, add more liquid. Serve hot, sprinkled with parsley, with a mixed salad.

peach filo baskets

SERVES **four** | 160 **6** ⑧

Prep: **15** minutes Cook: **8** minutes

The shops are full of ripe peaches and nectarines, so make the most of these juicy fruits. Why not treat yourself to this delicious dessert?

6 x 15 g/½ oz sheets filo pastry
1 egg, beaten
4 ripe peaches
60 g/2 oz mascarpone
85 g/3 oz 0% fat Greek yoghurt
icing sugar, for dusting

1 Take 4 small ceramic ramekin dishes and place them upside down on a baking sheet.

2 Cut each filo pastry sheet in half to form 2 squares, so you end up with 12 filo squares. Brush 3 squares with beaten egg, and place one of them over a ramekin dish, pressing it over the sides. Press 2 more squares down on top of it, at uneven angles. Repeat with the other 3 ramekins.

3 Bake in a preheated oven at 200°C, 400°F, Gas Mark 6 for about 8 minutes, until crisp and golden. Allow to cool before removing the baskets from the ramekins.

4 Stone the peaches and chop roughly. Mix the mascarpone and yoghurt and stir in the peaches. Divide the mixture between the filo baskets and serve dusted with icing sugar.

green risotto

SERVES two | 230 | 9 | 1

Prep: **15** minutes Cook: **25** minutes

Here's a great way of using up all those vegetables lurking in the bottom of your fridge. You can use any green vegetables in this citrus-flavoured herby risotto.

1 onion, finely chopped
1 leek, thinly sliced
2 garlic cloves, crushed
spray oil
115 g/4 oz Arborio or risotto rice
1 tablespoon dry white wine
400 ml/14 fl oz vegetable stock
60 g/2 oz shelled garden peas
85 g/3 oz runner beans, shredded
2 small courgettes, sliced
grated zest and juice of 1 lemon
2 tablespoons chopped parsley
a few chives, snipped
salt and ground black pepper
2 teaspoons grated Parmesan cheese

1 Gently cook the onion, leek and garlic in a deep frying pan which has been sprayed with oil. When they are tender, stir in the rice and the white wine.

2 Let it bubble up briefly and then start adding the hot stock, a little at a time. Cook gently over a low heat, adding more stock and stirring as the rice absorbs it and swells up.

3 Add the peas, runner beans and courgettes, and cook for 5 more minutes until softened. Stir in the lemon zest and juice and herbs and season to taste.

4 Take the risotto off the heat and let it stand for 5 minutes before serving, sprinkled with Parmesan, with a tomato salad.

scallop, bacon and rocket salad

SERVES two | 175 | 7 | 4

Prep: **15** minutes Cook: **5–6** minutes

Most supermarkets now sell fresh as well as frozen scallops. Because they are very meaty and low in fat, they make a very healthy meal. Take care not to overcook them or they will lose their juicy tenderness.

3 rashers extra thin lean back bacon, fat removed
6 large scallops
1 pack rocket
3 spring onions, finely chopped
4 cherry tomatoes, halved
3 tablespoons chopped parsley
2 tablespoons oil-free vinaigrette dressing
grated zest and juice of 1 lemon
salt and ground black pepper
chives, to garnish

1 With the blade of a knife stretch out each bacon rasher and then cut in half. Wrap each piece of bacon around a scallop.

2 Cook under a preheated grill for 5–6 minutes, turning them occasionally, until the scallops are cooked but still tender.

3 Mix together the rocket, onions, tomatoes and parsley. Blend the dressing with the lemon zest and juice and toss the salad.

4 Arrange a pile of salad on each serving plate with the bacon-wrapped scallops on top. Season and garnish with chives. If eating this as a main meal instead of a starter or light lunch, serve with boiled rice (100 cals, 4 Checks, 0.5 g fat for each 30 g/1 oz dry weight or 75 g/2½ oz cooked weight) or some crusty multi-grain bread (120 cals, 5 Checks, 2g fat per thick slice).

chicken with lemon couscous

SERVES **two** | 325 **13** ④

Prep: **15** minutes Cook: **25–35** minutes

2 x 150 g/5 oz skinless, boneless chicken breasts
2 courgettes, sliced diagonally
1 small aubergine, sliced
spray oil
salt and ground black pepper

Lemon couscous:
100 g/3½ oz couscous
350 ml/12 fl oz boiling chicken or vegetable stock
small bunch of thin spring onions, finely chopped
grated zest and juice of 1 large lemon
small bunch of mint, chopped
few sprigs of coriander, chopped

1 Put the couscous in a large basin and pour the boiling stock over the top. Set aside until the couscous grains have soaked up all the liquid.

2 Meanwhile, cook the chicken breasts for about 10–15 minutes each side in a hot ridged grill pan which has been sprayed lightly with oil.

3 When the chicken is cooked, remove and set aside while you char-grill the sliced courgettes and aubergine on both sides in the ridged pan. This takes about 5 minutes. Remove and sprinkle with salt and pepper.

4 Stir the spring onions, lemon zest and juice and chopped herbs into the warm couscous and serve with the grilled chicken and vegetables.

OR...

Instead of using lemon as a flavouring for the couscous, mix the grains with 3 ripe tomatoes which have been finely chopped, 6 chopped black olives, ¼ cucumber (chopped) and a finely chopped small red onion. Mix in a generous handful of chopped parsley and a diced mango, and you will have 390 cals, 16 Checks, 6 g fat per serving. Delicious!

You can serve this fresh, tangy couscous with any grilled meat or fish. If you can find a jar of preserved lemons, try chopping some up and mixing it into the couscous for a seriously lemony and authentic flavour.

grilled sardines with redcurrant salad

SERVES **two** | 340 | 14 | 18 |

Prep: **15** minutes Chill: **15** minutes Cook: **6–8** minutes

*Don't be put off by this
unusual combination
of fish and fruit – it
works incredibly well.
Buy ready-prepared
gutted fresh sardines to
make your life easier.*

6 fresh sardines, prepared and cleaned

2 garlic cloves, crushed

1 small red chilli, de-seeded and shredded

juice of ½ lemon

salt and ground black pepper

Redcurrant salad:

mixed salad leaves

¼ small red onion, chopped

¼ cucumber, diced

4 cherry tomatoes, halved

85 g/3 oz redcurrants

85 g/3 oz reduced-fat feta cheese, diced

1 teaspoon redcurrant jelly

2 tablespoons oil-free vinaigrette dressing

1 Place the sardines in a shallow dish with the garlic, chilli and lemon juice. Season with some salt and pepper, and coat the sardines with the chilli mixture. Cover with clingfilm and chill in the refrigerator for about 15 minutes.

2 Meanwhile, put the salad leaves, onion, cucumber, tomatoes, redcurrants and feta cheese in a bowl. Blend the redcurrant jelly with the dressing.

3 Lift the sardines out of the chilli marinade and cook under a preheated hot grill or over hot coals on a barbecue for about 3–4 minutes each side, until cooked through with opaque flesh and crisp skin.

4 Toss the prepared redcurrant salad in the dressing and serve immediately with the hot sardines.

OR...

You can cook other oily fish, such as mackerel or herring, in the same way. Just marinate and chill as outlined above and then cook under a grill, in a ridged grill pan or on a barbecue. Remember that larger fish will take longer to cook – they are ready to eat when the flesh is opaque and flakes easily.

Bourbon glazed steak kebabs

SERVES **two** | 235 **9** **6**

Prep: **10** minutes Chill: **2** hours Cook: **5–10** minutes

It's August and that means sunny days and barbecues. Marinating the steak like this not only makes it more succulent but also gives it a fabulous flavour. Instead of buying individual steaks, ask your butcher for a thick piece which you can cut into chunks.

300 g/10 oz really lean piece rump steak, all fat removed
2 small red onions, peeled and quartered
6 button mushrooms
1 small green pepper, de-seeded and cut into chunks

Bourbon marinade:

2 tablespoons Bourbon whisky
1 tablespoon tomato ketchup
1 teaspoon Dijon mustard
1 garlic clove, crushed
1 teaspoon runny honey
squeeze of lemon juice
few drops Worcestershire sauce

1 Mix all the marinade ingredients together. Cut the steak into bite-sized cubes and toss in the marinade. Cover and chill for at least 2 hours, or overnight if wished.

2 Thread the marinated steak, red onions, button mushrooms and green pepper on to 4 kebab skewers. If using wooden ones, soak them first in cold water.

3 Cook the kebabs over hot coals on a barbecue, turning them frequently and brushing with marinade. They will need 5–10 minutes, depending on how well done you like your steak.

4 Serve hot with grilled summer vegetables and some boiled rice flavoured with chopped herbs (100 cals, 4 Checks, 0.5 g fat for each 30 g/1 oz dry weight or 75 g/2½ oz cooked weight).

blueberry muffins

MAKES **12** | 175 **7** **6**

Prep: **15** minutes Cook: **20** minutes

Vary the fruit in these light little muffins depending on what's in season. Raspberries, blackberries or even strawberries work well, or you could use fresh cranberries in the winter months.

250 g/9 oz plain flour
2 teaspoons baking powder
½ teaspoon bicarbonate of soda
pinch of salt
100 g/3½ oz caster sugar
200 g/7 oz plain low-fat yoghurt
75 g/2½ oz melted butter
1 medium egg, beaten
125 g/4½ oz blueberries

1 Sift the flour, baking powder and bicarbonate of soda into a mixing bowl. Mix in the salt and sugar.

2 Blend the yoghurt with the melted butter and beaten egg, and stir into the dry ingredients until thoroughly mixed. Fold in the blueberries to distribute them evenly through the mixture.

3 Line a muffin tray with 12 paper cases and divide the mixture between them. Bake in a preheated oven at 190°C, 375°F, Gas Mark 5 for about 20 minutes, until well risen and golden. Cool on a wire rack.

autumn

A week's main meals for autumn

Sicilian mussel soup

SERVES **four** | 120 **5** **3**

Prep: **15** minutes Cook: **25** minutes

Now that mussels are coming back into season, how about making a healthy, nutritious soup. You can enjoy this for a light lunch or serve it with bread and a salad as a more substantial evening meal.

1 kg/2 lb fresh mussels in their shells
1 onion, finely chopped
2 garlic cloves, crushed
1 leek, thinly sliced
spray oil
1 fresh chilli, de-seeded and chopped
1 x 400 g/14 oz can chopped tomatoes
300 ml/½ pint hot fish or vegetable stock
salt and ground black pepper
2 tablespoons parsley, chopped

1 Put the mussels in the sink or a large bowl of cold water. Discard any that are open, damaged or cracked. Scrub the remaining mussels well, removing the 'beards' with a sharp knife. Set aside while you make the soup.

2 Cook the onion, garlic and leek in a large saucepan sprayed with oil over a medium heat, until softened. Add the chilli and tomatoes and cook for 5 minutes. Add the stock and seasoning and bring to the boil.

3 Over a high heat, add the mussels. Cover with a lid and cook for 3–5 minutes, shaking the pan occasionally, until the mussels open. Discard any that fail to open.

4 Sprinkle with parsley, check the seasoning and ladle into deep bowls. Serve piping hot.

leeks niçoise

SERVES **two** | 55 **2** **4**

Prep: **10** minutes Cook: **8–10** minutes

Before the warm days finally come to an end and the nights turn colder, try this light lunch dish from Provence. You can serve green beans or asparagus in the same way. Don't worry if you have no honey mustard – use English or Dijon instead.

450 g/1 lb slim leeks
3 tablespoons oil-free vinaigrette dressing
1 teaspoon honey mustard
pinch of sugar
salt and ground black pepper
1 hard-boiled egg, peeled and chopped
6 black olives, stoned
1 tablespoon chopped parsley

1 Trim the leeks and remove any tough dark green leaves. Wash them thoroughly under running cold water to remove any grit and dirt.

2 Cook the whole leeks in a large pan of boiling salted water for 8–10 minutes, until they are cooked and tender but not mushy – they must retain their shape. Drain and pat dry with kitchen paper.

3 Mix the vinaigrette dressing with the honey mustard, a pinch of sugar and some salt and pepper. Arrange the hot leeks in a shallow dish and pour the dressing over the top. Sprinkle with chopped egg, tuck in the olives and scatter over the parsley. Serve warm or chilled.

tagliatelle with garlic mushrooms

SERVES **two** 310 12 10

Prep: **10** minutes Cook: **15** minutes

150 g/5 oz tagliatelle

1 small onion, finely chopped

3 fat garlic cloves, cut into slivers

spray oil

225 g/8 oz chestnut mushrooms, thinly sliced

2 tablespoons dry white wine or vermouth

4 tablespoons half-fat crème fraîche

salt and ground black pepper

small bunch of flat-leaf parsley, chopped

1 Cook the pasta in a large saucepan of boiling salted water for about 8–10 minutes, according to the package instructions. Drain well.

2 While the pasta is cooking, gently cook the onion and garlic in the spray oil in a large frying pan until tender and golden. Add the sliced mushrooms and cook, turning occasionally, for 5 minutes, until golden.

3 Add the wine or vermouth and let it bubble up and evaporate, then stir in the crème fraîche and heat through very gently over a low heat. Season to taste and toss the cooked pasta in this creamy sauce with the parsley. Serve immediately.

OR...

You can use any pasta shapes or even spaghetti or linguine in this dish – whatever you have in your store cupboard. If you sprinkle it with grated Parmesan, remember to add 20 cals, 1 Check, 2 fat grams per dessertspoon. To make it into something really special, if you can get hold of any wild mushrooms, use them instead of cultivated ones – the flavour will be out of this world!

This delicious supper is so cheap to make and also really quick and easy. It's perfect when you are tired after work and want some simple comfort food.

Persian chicken pilaff

SERVES **two** 340 14 ③

Prep: **10** minutes Soak: **1** hour Cook: **35** minutes

The turmeric in this spicy dish gives it a wonderful golden colour and a subtle flavour, which serves to complement the other aromatic spices used.

115 g/4 oz basmati rice
spray oil
1 onion, finely chopped
2 cardamom pods
1 teaspoon cumin seeds
1 teaspoon turmeric powder
pinch of allspice
175 g/6 oz chicken breast fillets, sliced
1 tablespoon currants
salt and ground black pepper
2 tablespoons chopped fresh coriander
4 tablespoons low-fat plain yoghurt

1 Tip the rice into a bowl and cover it with cold water. Leave to soak for at least 1 hour, then drain well.

2 Heat a large saucepan that has been lightly sprayed with oil. Add the onion and cook for about 5 minutes until soft and golden. Scrape the cardamom seeds out of the pods and add to the onion with the cumin, turmeric and allspice. Cook for 1–2 minutes to release the flavour.

3 Add the chicken and cook for about 5 minutes, stirring until browned all over. Stir in the currants and the drained rice. Cook for 2 minutes, stirring.

4 Add 300 ml/½ pint hot water and stir well. Season with salt and pepper and cover the pan. Cook very gently over a low heat for 20 minutes, until the rice is cooked. Don't worry if a crust of golden rice forms on the bottom – it's delicious.

5 Check the seasoning and serve the pilaff sprinkled with coriander and topped with yoghurt.

OR...

You can use the same quantity of lean lamb (the leg steaks or fillet are best, cut into cubes) instead of chicken. This will give you 370 cals, 15 Checks, 8 g fat per serving. Vegetarians can omit the meat altogether and serve the pilaff topped with some grilled peppers, courgettes, aubergine or mushrooms and cherry tomatoes (240 cals, 10 Checks, 1 g fat per serving).

pork with apricot stuffing

SERVES **four** | 260 10 8

Prep: **10** minutes Cook: **30** minutes

Autumn's here and it's time for a roast of lean succulent pork and some new season's apples, whether they're from the supermarket, farmers' market or just some windfalls from your garden.

500 g/1 lb 2 oz lean pork fillet in one piece, visible fat removed

4 fresh apricots, halved and stoned

4 sage leaves

spray oil

1 teaspoon sea salt flakes

freshly ground black pepper

4 dessert apples, cored

150 ml/¼ pint dry cider

1 tablespoon low-fat crème fraîche

1 With a sharp knife, make a deep cut along one side of the pork fillet, leaving the ends intact. Place the apricots and sage leaves in the slit. Close the fillet like a book and secure with string to hold in the filling.

2 Place the fillet in a roasting pan, spray with oil and then sprinkle with sea salt and plenty of black pepper. Bake in the preheated oven at 200°C, 400°F, Gas Mark 6 for 15 minutes.

3 Score the apples horizontally round the middle and tuck them in around the pork. Pour the cider over the top and then return to the oven for about 15–20 minutes, until the pork is cooked and the apples are tender.

4 Remove the pork and apples and keep warm while you boil up and reduce any pan juices on top of the stove. Stir in the crème fraîche.

5 Remove the string from the pork and carve into slices. Serve with the baked apples and pan juices, with steamed carrots and green vegetables.

plums poached in red wine

SERVES **four** | 65 25 0

Prep: **5** minutes Cook: **15** minutes

There are so many different varieties of plums to choose from in September. Choose some really plump, ripe and juicy ones for this dessert. You can serve it hot or cold.

150 ml/¼ pint fruity red wine

2 whole cloves

1 cinnamon stick

1 strip of orange rind

450 g/1 lb plums, stoned if wished

artificial sweetener, to taste

1 Pour the red wine into a saucepan with the spices and orange rind. Bring to the boil, then reduce the heat and simmer very gently for about 5 minutes. Add the plums and cook very gently until tender. Remove with a slotted spoon.

2 Boil the liquid for 2–3 minutes to reduce it down to a syrup. Remove from the heat, then sweeten to taste with artificial sweetener, and discard the orange rind and spices.

3 Pour the syrup over the plums and serve warm or chilled with low-fat yoghurt or a scoop of low-fat vanilla ice cream.

butternut squash chunky chowder

SERVES six | 60 25 3

Prep: **10** minutes Cook: **25–30** minutes

If you're not going to eat all the soup, just freeze what's left over in individual portions. Vegetarians can leave out the bacon.

115 g/4 oz lean smoked bacon, chopped

1 onion, finely chopped

2 garlic cloves, crushed

2 leeks, trimmed and sliced

1 large butternut squash, peeled, de-seeded and cut into chunks

1 tablespoon plain flour

300 ml/½ pint vegetable stock

300 ml/½ pint semi-skimmed milk

3 ripe red tomatoes, quartered

1 bay leaf

salt and ground black pepper

4 tablespoons chopped parsley

1 Cook the bacon in a saucepan, stirring occasionally, until golden. Add the onion, garlic, leeks and squash and cook over a low heat for 5 minutes, until softened.

2 Stir in the flour and cook for 1 minute. Gradually stir in the stock and milk and then bring to the boil. Reduce the heat, add the tomatoes and bay leaf and cook for 10–15 minutes.

3 Season to taste with salt and pepper and stir in the parsley. Serve hot ladled into bowls.

OR...

Omit the bacon and you really will have a slimming soup – only 25 cals, 1 Check, 0 g fat per serving!

prawn and aubergine curry

SERVES two | 200 8 10

Prep: **10** minutes Cook: **20** minutes

Depending on which sort of Thai curry you prefer, you can use green or red curry paste in this recipe. If you feel very adventurous, make your own by whizzing some fresh chillies, lemon grass, garlic, root ginger and coriander to a thick paste in a blender.

1 small onion or 2 shallots, thinly sliced

2.5 cm/1 in piece fresh root ginger, peeled and chopped

spray oil

1 aubergine, thinly sliced

2 tablespoons Thai curry paste

6 cherry tomatoes, halved

150 ml/¼ pint reduced-fat coconut milk

1 teaspoon nam pla (Thai fish sauce)

175 g/6 oz peeled raw tiger prawns

2 tablespoons chopped fresh coriander

few basil leaves, shredded

1 Cook the onion or shallots with the ginger in a frying pan which has been sprayed lightly with oil. When they are golden and translucent, add the aubergine and cook gently until tender and golden on both sides.

2 Stir in the curry paste and cook for 1 minute, then add the tomatoes and cook for 2–3 minutes. Pour in the coconut milk and nam pla, and heat through gently.

3 Add the prawns and cook until they turn pink on both sides. Scatter with fresh coriander and basil, and then serve with some plain boiled rice (100 cals, 4 Checks, 0.5 g fat for each 30 g/1 oz dry weight or 75 g/2½ oz cooked weight).

Spanish-style pork with beans

SERVES **two** | 310 | 12 ⑩

Prep: **10** minutes Cook: **25** minutes

300 g/10 oz lean pork fillet, any visible fat removed

½ teaspoon crushed chilli flakes

2 tablespoons Spanish sherry vinegar

200 g/7 oz field or chestnut mushrooms, quartered or sliced

1 x 200 g/7 oz can haricot or cannellini beans, drained

3 garlic cloves, crushed

juice of 1 large sweet orange

salt and ground black pepper

paprika, for dusting

2 tablespoons chopped parsley

1 Place the pork fillet in an ovenproof dish or roasting pan and scatter with chilli flakes. Season lightly with salt and pepper and pour the vinegar over the top.

2 Roast in a preheated oven at 210°C, 425°F, Gas Mark 7 for 10 minutes. Remove from the oven, turn the pork fillet over, and add the mushrooms, drained beans, garlic and orange juice. Return to the oven and cook for a further 15 minutes, until the pork is cooked through.

3 Arrange the beans and mushrooms in the pan juices on 2 serving plates. Carve the pork thinly and place the slices on top of the bean mixture. Dust lightly with paprika, scatter with parsley and serve immediately.

OR...

Chicken works equally well in this delicious recipe. Instead of pork, roast 2 skinned, boneless 150 g/5 oz chicken breasts in the same way. Serve with colourful grilled red, yellow and green pepper strips (235 cals, 9 Checks, 4 g fat per serving). Because it is quite low in calories, you can make this meal more substantial by eating it with a mound of plain boiled rice to soak up the juices (100 cals, 4 Checks, 0.5 g fat for each 30 g/1 oz dry weight or 75 g/2½ oz cooked weight).

The beauty of this simple supper is that it is all cooked in the same dish. Enjoy seasonal mushrooms now while they are cheap and plentiful – wild ones will taste even better than the cultivated sort.

quick coq au vin

SERVES **two** | 260 **10** ⑤

Prep: **10** minutes Cook: **45** minutes

You can cheat with the usual recipe for this classic French dish and thereby reduce not only the calories but also the cooking time. You can make coq au vin in advance, if wished, cool it thoroughly and then refrigerate it.

1 onion, finely chopped
2 garlic cloves, crushed
spray oil
115 g/4 oz tiny button mushrooms
4 chicken thighs, skinned
1 teaspoon plain flour
150 ml/¼ pint red wine
150 ml/¼ pint chicken stock
2 large ripe tomatoes, chopped
1 bay leaf
2 sprigs of rosemary
2 sprigs of thyme
salt and ground black pepper
1 tablespoon chopped parsley

1 Cook the onion and garlic in a flameproof casserole or heavy saucepan, which has been sprayed lightly with oil. When soft and golden, add the mushrooms and cook for 3–4 minutes until lightly browned. Add the chicken thighs and cook on both sides until golden brown.

2 Stir in the flour, cook for 1 minute and then add the wine and chicken stock. Stir well and add the tomatoes and herbs.

3 Bring to the boil, then lower the heat to a simmer and cover the pan. Cook gently for about 30 minutes, until the chicken is cooked right through. Check the seasoning, sprinkle with parsley and serve with steamed carrots and green vegetables.

mushroom lasagne

SERVES **two** | 350 **14** ③

Prep: **15** minutes Cook: **45** minutes

Use cultivated button or chestnut mushrooms in this dish, or some wild ones if you can get hold of them. You can buy dried ceps in most supermarkets.

45 g/1½ oz dried ceps (mushrooms)
1 small onion, finely chopped
spray oil
350 g/12 oz mushrooms, sliced
2 tablespoons chopped parsley
6 sheets pre-cooked lasagne
salt and ground black pepper
2 tablespoons grated Parmesan cheese

White sauce:
2 tablespoons cornflour
300 ml/½ pint skimmed milk
150 ml/¼ pint very low fat fromage frais
pinch of ground nutmeg

1 Put the ceps in a jug, pour over boiling water and stand for 15 minutes. Drain.

2 Cook the onion in a hot frying pan sprayed with oil until softened. Add the mushrooms and cook until tender. Add the drained ceps, parsley and seasoning.

3 Make the white sauce: blend the cornflour with some of the milk. Bring the remaining milk to the boil and stir in the cornflour mixture. Cook for 1–2 minutes, stirring until thick. Off the heat, beat in the fromage frais and nutmeg.

4 Place 2 lasagne sheets in the base of a small baking dish. Cover with half the mushroom mixture, then cover with 2 more lasagne sheets. Pour half the white sauce over the top and then the remaining mushrooms. Cover with the last 2 lasagne sheets and pour over the rest of the sauce. Sprinkle with Parmesan. Bake in a preheated oven at 190°C, 375°F, Gas Mark 5 for 25 minutes, until golden

open ravioli with ragu

SERVES **two** | 320 | 13 | 6

Prep: **10** minutes Cook: **1¼** hours

Why not try this low-fat alternative to lasagne, which is quicker and easier to make? If you are a veggie, you could use some Quorn mince instead of beef.

1 small onion, chopped
2 garlic cloves, crushed
1 carrot, diced
1 stick celery, chopped
spray oil
200 g/7 oz minced beef (max. 5% fat)
1 tablespoon tomato paste
90 ml/3 fl oz red wine
115 ml/4 fl oz skimmed milk
1 x 200 g/7 oz can chopped Italian tomatoes
1 bay leaf
few sprigs of thyme
salt and ground black pepper
4 lasagne sheets
1 sprig fresh rosemary, chopped

1 Sweat the chopped onion, garlic, carrot and celery in a large saucepan which has been sprayed with oil for about 5 minutes, until softened. Add the minced beef and cook, stirring, until browned all over.

2 Stir in the tomato paste, red wine and milk and then bring to the boil. Reduce the heat and add the tomatoes, herbs and seasoning. Simmer gently for about 1 hour until the sauce has reduced and thickened. Check the seasoning.

3 Cook the lasagne sheets in a large pan of boiling salted water, according to the packet instructions, until tender. Drain well.

4 Place a sheet of lasagne on each serving plate. Spoon the sauce over the top and cover with the remaining sheets of lasagne. Sprinkle with fresh chopped rosemary and serve at once with a green salad.

autumn fruit crumble

SERVES **six** | 190 | 8 | 7

Prep: **15** minutes Cook: **30** minutes

If you can get your hands on some windfall apples and explore the local hedgerows for blackberries, this is a really economical pudding – and what could possibly be more autumnal? So go on, treat yourself!

700 g/1½ lb cooking apples, peeled, cored and sliced
225 g/8 oz fresh blackberries
artificial sweetener
115 g/4 oz plain flour
50 g/1¾ oz butter, softened
good pinch of ground cinnamon
30 g/1 oz icing sugar, sifted

1 Put the apples and blackberries in an ovenproof baking dish and sprinkle with artificial sweetener to taste.

2 Sift the flour into a large mixing bowl. Cut the butter into tiny pieces and add to the flour. Rub in with your fingertips until the mixture resembles fine breadcrumbs. Stir in the cinnamon and icing sugar together with 1 tablespoon cold water.

3 Spoon the crumble over the fruit and smooth the top. Bake in a preheated oven at 190°C, 375°F, Gas Mark 5 for 30 minutes, until the crumble is cooked and golden and the fruit is tender.

4 Serve hot with reduced-fat ice cream (45 cals, 2 Checks, 1.5 g fat per level scoop).

spiced pumpkin and butter bean soup

SERVES six | 35 15 ⊙

Prep: **15** minutes Cook: **35** minutes

Pumpkin is in season and it's superb in soup. This is the perfect warming supper for Bonfire Night – and you can even use the scooped-out pumpkin from your grinning jack o' lanterns.

2 onions, chopped

1 garlic clove, crushed

1 red chilli, de-seeded and chopped

spray oil

500 g/1 lb 2 oz pumpkin flesh, cut into cubes

900 ml/1½ pints vegetable stock

pinch each of ground nutmeg and cumin

1 x 400 g/14 oz can butter beans, drained

salt and ground black pepper

6 teaspoons low-fat plain yoghurt

2 tablespoons chopped parsley

1 Cook the onions, garlic and chilli in a large saucepan sprayed with oil. When the onions are translucent and softened, add the pumpkin and cook for about 3 minutes, turning it occasionally.

2 Add the vegetable stock, bring to the boil, then reduce the heat to a simmer and cook gently for 15 minutes until the pumpkin is cooked and tender.

3 Liquidize in batches in a blender. Pour the smooth, golden soup into a clean pan and stir in the ground spices and butter beans. Season to taste and heat through gently.

4 Serve the soup hot in bowls, topped with a swirl of yoghurt and sprinkled with parsley.

pot-roast pheasant

SERVES three | 300 12 ⑧

Prep: **10** minutes Cook: **1** hour

Pheasant may sound rather grand but it's actually relatively inexpensive, highly nutritious and low in fat. You can buy it at your local butcher or most supermarkets.

1 plump oven-ready pheasant, skin removed

spray oil

3 garlic cloves, peeled

1 onion, sliced

2 celery sticks, chopped

1 carrot, diced

1 teaspoon plain flour

125 ml/4 fl oz white vermouth or dry white wine

125 ml/4 fl oz chicken stock

sprigs of thyme and sage

salt and ground black pepper

2 tablespoons chopped parsley

1 Wash the pheasant under cold running water and pat dry. Season with salt and pepper inside and out.

2 Heat a flameproof casserole sprayed with oil and brown the pheasant, turning often until golden. Remove and set aside.

3 Add the garlic and vegetables to the casserole and cook until softened. Stir in the flour and add the vermouth and stock. Bring to the boil, then add the herbs and the pheasant.

4 Cover with a lid and cook in a preheated oven at 190°C, 375°F, Gas Mark 5 for 40–45 minutes, until the pheasant is cooked.

5 Cut the pheasant into pieces and serve with the cooked vegetables and juices, sprinkled with parsley. A baked potato goes well with this dish.

bonfire bangers with apple mash

SERVES **two** | 355 | 14 | 7

Prep: **15** minutes Cook: **20** minutes

You could substitute Quorn sausages for the low-fat ones in this great recipe. If you are having fireworks and a bonfire party, just increase the quantities accordingly.

1 teaspoon runny honey

2 teaspoons grain mustard

4 large low-fat sausages

2 dessert apples, cored and scored round the middle

2 large onions, thinly sliced

½ teaspoon cumin seeds

spray oil

300 g/10 oz peeled potatoes

60 ml/2 fl oz skimmed milk

2 tablespoons low-fat crème fraîche

salt and ground black pepper

1 Mix the honey with 1 teaspoon of grain mustard, and use this to coat the sausages. Place them in a roasting pan with the apples, and cook in a preheated oven at 200°C, 400°F, Gas Mark 6 for about 20 minutes, turning occasionally.

2 Cook the onions and cumin seeds in a pan sprayed with oil over a low heat until they are softened, golden and melting.

3 At the same time, cook the potatoes in a pan of boiling salted water until cooked and tender but not mushy.

4 Drain the potatoes, then tip them back into the pan with the milk. Mash or beat with an electric whisk until smooth. Beat in the crème fraîche, remaining grain mustard and seasoning.

5 Scoop out the flesh from the baked apples and mix with the onions. Serve the sausages with the potato topped with the apple mixture. Leeks, cabbage and broccoli go well with this.

spaghetti with sweet chilli scallops

SERVES **two** | 380 | 15 | 3

Prep: **5** minutes Cook: **10** minutes

This delicious way of serving pasta is so quick and easy but posh enough to serve to guests at a formal dinner party.

150 g/5 oz spaghetti or thin angel's hair pasta

spray oil

8 king scallops, with corals, halved

1 garlic clove, crushed

2 ripe tomatoes, skinned and chopped

1 teaspoon sweet chilli sauce

juice of 1 lemon

salt and ground black pepper

rocket or watercress, to serve

1 Cook the pasta in a large saucepan of boiling salted water, according to the manufacturer's instructions, until just tender but not mushy. Drain well.

2 Meanwhile, spray a small frying pan with oil and cook the scallops over a medium heat for about 2 minutes each side, until tender – do not overcook or they will be tough.

3 Add the garlic, tomatoes, chilli sauce, lemon juice and some salt and a good grinding of black pepper. Cook for 1 minute.

4 Toss the drained pasta with the scallop mixture and divide between 2 plates. Serve with a garnish of rocket or watercress.

pesto beanburgers

SERVES | two | 280 | **11** | ⑫

Prep: **15** minutes   Chill: **20–30** minutes   Cook: **10** minutes

1 x 400 g/14 oz can cannellini
beans, rinsed and drained

1 small onion, finely chopped

1 garlic clove, crushed

1 red chilli, de-seeded and finely
chopped

1 tablespoon red pesto sauce

few sprigs of fresh coriander or
parsley

1 medium egg, beaten

30 g/1 oz reduced-fat Cheddar
cheese, grated

2 tablespoons virtually fat-free
fromage frais

salt and ground black pepper

flour for dusting

spray oil

1 Put the cannellini beans in a food processor or blender with the onion, garlic, chilli, pesto sauce, herbs, beaten egg, cheese and fromage frais. Add some seasoning and blend quickly to a stiff paste. If you prefer beanburgers with a rougher texture, you can mash the beans coarsely with a potato masher instead and then stir in the other ingredients. Cover and chill in the refrigerator until ready to cook.

2 Divide the mixture into 4 portions and shape each one into a patty with your hands. Dust lightly with flour.

3 Spray a large shallow pan with oil and place over a low to medium heat. When it's really hot, add the beanburgers and cook gently for about 5 minutes each side until the burgers are crisp and golden brown.

4 Serve immediately with some sweet chilli sauce (30 cals, 1 Check, 0 g fat for 1 level dessertspoon) or fruit chutney and a watercress or chicory salad.

OR...

You could serve each burger with salad leaves and sliced tomato in a seeded burger bun, in which case you should add on 155 cals, 6 Checks, 3 fat grams per bun.

You don't have to be a committed vegetarian to appreciate these delicious beanburgers. If you don't have any cannellini beans in your store cupboard, then use haricot or butterbeans instead.

chicken with wild mushrooms

SERVES two | 180 | 7 | 3

Prep: **5** minutes Cook: **35** minutes

Fresh wild mushrooms tend to be quite expensive, but they are worth it if you can find them. However, this recipe uses a mixture of fresh cultivated and dried ceps to make it more affordable.

2 x 115 g/4 oz skinless, boneless chicken breasts
300 ml/½ pint chicken stock
20 g/⅔ oz dried ceps (mushrooms)
1 small onion, finely chopped
150 g/5 oz chestnut or button mushrooms, sliced
spray oil
150 g/5 oz natural yoghurt
salt and freshly ground black pepper
1 tablespoon chopped parsley

1 Simmer the chicken breasts in the chicken stock in a saucepan over a low to medium heat for about 20 minutes, until cooked through. Remove the chicken and keep warm.

2 Add the dried ceps to the stock in the pan and then boil hard until reduced by half.

3 Cook the onion and sliced mushrooms in a frying pan which has been sprayed with oil, until softened. Stir in the reduced stock and ceps and cook for 2–3 minutes. Stir in the yoghurt and season to taste. Heat through gently without boiling.

4 Serve the chicken with the mushroom sauce sprinkled with parsley. Plain boiled rice or pasta ribbons go well with this dish (100 cals, 4 Checks, 0.5 g fat for each 30 g/1 oz dry weight or 75 g/2½ oz cooked weight).

baked apples with exotic fruits

SERVES two | 230 | 9 | 0

Prep: **10** minutes Cook: **30–40** minutes

While home-grown apples are still cheap and plentiful, treat yourself to this quick and easy pudding. Bramley apples, with their wonderful fluffy texture, are the best ones to use for baking.

2 large Bramley apples
juice of 1 orange and 1 lemon

Fruity filling:
2 medjool dates, pitted and chopped
2 dried apricots, chopped
1 tablespoon dried exotic fruits
grated zest and juice of 1 orange
15 g/½ oz light muscovado sugar

1 Mix all the ingredients for the filling together. Core the apples and, with a sharp knife, score each one horizontally around the middle.

2 Place the apples in a baking dish and fill the hollows with the filling mixture. Pour over the orange and lemon juice.

3 Bake in a preheated oven at 190°C, 375°F, Gas Mark 5 for 30–40 minutes, until the apples are cooked and fluffy. Baste them occasionally during cooking.

4 Serve immediately with low-fat yoghurt (25 cals, 1 Check, 0.5 g fat per rounded tablespoon), or reduced-fat ice cream (45 cals, 2 Checks, 1.5 g fat per level scoop).

winter

A week's main meals for winter

SERVES four | 115 5 ③ brussels sprout and chestnut soup

Prep: **10** minutes Cook: **35–40** minutes

The shops are now full of Brussels sprouts and chestnuts, so why not use them in a delicious, warming soup? If you don't want the hassle of peeling chestnuts, just use the vacuum-packed ones instead.

1 onion, finely chopped
225 g/8 oz shelled chestnuts
900 ml/1½ pints vegetable stock
good pinch of grated nutmeg
225 g/8 oz Brussels sprouts, shredded
salt and ground black pepper
45 ml/1½ fl oz half-fat crème fraîche
snipped chives, to garnish

1 Put the onion and chestnuts in a saucepan and barely cover with some of the vegetable stock. Season with salt and pepper, and simmer gently for 15–20 minutes, until the chestnuts are cooked and tender.

2 Add the nutmeg and shredded sprouts together with the remaining stock and bring to the boil. Reduce the heat and simmer gently for 15 minutes.

3 Liquidize the soup in batches in a blender, and then return to the pan. Stir in the crème fraîche and reheat gently. Serve hot garnished with chives.

SERVES two | 265 11 ② turkey satsuma stir-fry

Prep: **10** minutes Cook: **10** minutes

You can use fresh turkey breasts in this recipe or adapt it for using up the leftover Christmas bird – just cook the mushrooms, noodles and spring onions and then add the cooked shredded turkey with the juicy satsumas. Either way it tastes refreshing and delicious after a surfeit of rich festive food.

250 g/9 oz skinless turkey breast fillets, thinly sliced
1 garlic clove, crushed
½ teaspoon grated fresh root ginger
1 small red chilli, de-seeded and finely chopped (optional)
spray oil
175 g/6 oz mushrooms, sliced
4 spring onions, sliced
150 g/5 oz fresh egg noodles or 'straight-to-wok' noodles
1 tablespoon soy sauce
juice of 2 satsumas
peeled segments of 1 satsuma
salt and ground black pepper

1 Cook the turkey, garlic, ginger and chilli (if using) in a hot pan which has been sprayed lightly with oil for 3–4 minutes, stirring occasionally, until the turkey is golden. Add the mushrooms and spring onions and stir-fry for 2–3 minutes.

2 Stir in the noodles and cook for 2 minutes. Add the soy sauce, satsuma juice and segments, then stir and heat through. Check the seasoning.

3 Divide between 2 serving plates and serve immediately with some steamed pak choi or broccoli.

spiced beef with prunes

SERVES **two** | 230 9 6

Prep: **10** minutes Cook: **2¼** hours

A traditional casserole will warm you up on a cold day. Just prepare it in advance, pop it in the oven and forget about it for a couple of hours. The prunes add natural sweetness.

1 large onion, thinly sliced
1 stick celery, chopped
2 carrots, sliced
2 garlic cloves, crushed
2.5 cm/1 in piece fresh root ginger, peeled and chopped
spray oil
225 g/8 oz cubed lean braising steak, all visible fat removed
1 teaspoon ground cumin
1 teaspoon tomato paste
100 ml/3½ fl oz red wine
1 tablespoon red wine vinegar
200 ml/7 fl oz beef stock
1 bay leaf, sprigs of thyme and sage
6 ready-to-eat prunes
salt and ground black pepper
1 tablespoon chopped parsley

1 Cook the onion, celery, carrots, garlic and ginger over a medium heat in a flameproof casserole dish which has been sprayed with oil. When the vegetables are softened, stir in the cubes of beef and cumin. Cook, turning occasionally, until the meat is browned all over.

2 Stir in the tomato paste, wine, vinegar and stock. Add the herbs and bring to the boil, stirring. Remove from the heat, season with salt and pepper and add the prunes.

3 Cover the casserole with a lid and cook in a preheated oven at 170°C, 325°F, Gas Mark 3 for 2 hours. Check after 1½ hours and give it a stir to ensure the beef is covered. If it needs more liquid, add a little stock.

4 Remove the herbs, check the seasoning and serve hot, sprinkled with parsley, with some cabbage or sprouts.

bacon wrapped cod with red pesto

SERVES **two** | 255 10 15

Prep: **15** minutes Cook: **40** minutes

If you are doubtful about the merits of combining fish and meat ('surf and turf' as they call it in America), don't be – they work surprisingly well together. And this recipe is as easy as it gets for a great supper on a chilly evening.

1 small butternut squash, peeled, de-seeded and cubed
1 teaspoon chopped fresh sage
spray olive oil
2 x 125 g/4½ oz thick cod fillets
2 tablespoons red pesto sauce
4 rashers extra thin streaky bacon
6 cherry tomatoes
salt and ground black pepper

1 Put the butternut squash in a large roasting pan. Season lightly with salt and pepper, sprinkle over the sage and spray lightly with oil. Bake in a preheated oven at 220°C, 425°F, Gas Mark 8 for 25 minutes.

2 Spread the cod fillets with the pesto. With the blade of a knife, stretch out the bacon rashers and use to wrap the cod.

3 Place the cod fillets in the roasting pan with the squash. Tuck in the cherry tomatoes and bake for a further 12–15 minutes, until the cod is cooked through, the bacon is crisp and the squash is tender. Serve immediately with watercress.

SERVES **two** 215 **9** 13 # winter chicory salad

Prep: **10** minutes

Crisp white chicory or the red variety from Treviso is now in the shops and makes a tasty crunchy salad to accompany leftover cold turkey or ham. Salty Roquefort is the best blue cheese to use.

2 heads chicory
1 sweet red dessert apple
¼ red onion, finely chopped
1 baby avocado, peeled, stoned and diced
30 g/1 oz Roquefort cheese, diced
4 tablespoons canned chick peas
3–4 tablespoons chopped parsley
3 tablespoons oil-free vinaigrette dressing
1 teaspoon Dijon mustard
juice of 1 lemon

1 Trim the ends off the chicory and slice the heads thinly into rounds. Core the apple and cut into dice or thin slices.

2 Mix the chicory, apple, red onion, avocado, Roquefort, chick peas and parsley in a bowl.

3 Blend the oil-free dressing with the honey mustard and lemon juice and season to taste with salt and pepper. Pour over the chicory salad and toss gently. Enjoy!

SERVES **eight** 165 **7** 10 # chocolate yule log

Prep: **20** minutes Cook: **8–10** minutes

The festive season does not have to ruin your efforts to achieve your target weight. This delicious chocolate log is proof that you can still enjoy some seasonal favourites without spoiling your weight loss efforts.

3 eggs
60 g/2 oz caster sugar
85 g/3 oz self-raising flour
1 tablespoon cocoa powder
icing sugar for dusting

Filling and coating:
110 ml/4 fl oz double cream
200 g/7 oz low-fat fromage frais
4 teaspoons cocoa powder

1 Lightly grease a Swiss roll tin and line with non-stick baking paper. Beat the eggs and sugar until the mixture is pale and fluffy. Sift in the flour and cocoa powder and fold in lightly but thoroughly in a figure-of-eight movement.

2 Spread out the mixture in the prepared tin, levelling the surface, and bake in a preheated oven at 200°C, 400°F, Gas Mark 6 for 8–10 minutes.

3 Turn out the sponge on a large sheet of greaseproof paper. Peel away the lining paper, cover with a clean damp tea towel and set aside to cool.

4 Whip the cream and fold in the fromage frais. Blend the cocoa with 4 teaspoons hot water and stir into the creamy mixture.

5 Spread half of the chocolate cream over the sponge, and roll up from one long end. Place on a serving plate and cover with the remaining chocolate mixture. Draw some lines through it to resemble a log. Dust with icing sugar and cut into slices.

split pea and ham soup

SERVES **six** | 175 | **7** | ②

Soak: **2** hours   Prep: **15** minutes   Cook: **2¼** hours

225 g/8 oz green split peas
1 onion, chopped
2 carrots, diced
1 celery stick, chopped
1 leek, trimmed and chopped
spray oil
1200 ml/2 pints vegetable stock
1 bay leaf
leaves from 2 sprigs of thyme
225 g/8 oz lean ham, chopped
(visible fat removed)
salt and ground black pepper
4 teaspoons low-fat yoghurt

1 Put the split peas in a bowl, cover with plenty of cold water and soak for at least 2 hours.

2 Cook the onion, carrots, celery and leek in a large saucepan sprayed with oil until tender. Stir in the drained split peas and cook for 30 seconds. Add the stock and bring to the boil.

3 Reduce the heat to a simmer and then add the herbs and seasoning. Cover and simmer gently for 2 hours, until the peas have cooked down and thickened the soup. If the soup is too thick, thin it with a little stock.

4 Add the ham about 30 minutes before the end of cooking time. Serve in bowls with a decorative swirl of yoghurt on top.

This soup is so filling and nourishing that you could eat it for your main meal. If you can't buy green split peas, you can use the yellow ones instead.

orange glazed fish

SERVES **two** | 375 | **15** | ②

Prep: **5** minutes   Cook: **20** minutes

2 x 150 g/5 oz white fish fillets,
e.g. cod, swordfish or hoki
1 tablespoon sweet chilli sauce
grated zest and juice of 1 large
orange
2 spring onions, finely shredded
125 g/4½ oz rice noodles
salt and ground black pepper
2 tablespoons chopped parsley or
coriander

1 Place the fish fillets on a sheet of foil and wrap up loosely to make a sealed parcel. Cook on a baking tray in a preheated oven at 180°C, 350°F, Gas Mark 4 for 10 minutes.

2 Mix the chilli sauce with the orange zest and juice and spring onions. Remove the fish from the oven and open up the parcel. Spoon the chilli orange mixture over the top. With the foil left open, bake for 10 minutes.

3 Cook the noodles according to the packet instructions and divide between 2 plates. Place a fish fillet on each, season and sprinkle with herbs. Serve with steamed pak choi or spinach.

The shops are full of the new season's large Navel oranges. At this time of year, they are at their best. You can cook salmon fillets the same way, although one 100 g/3½ oz fillet will add 100 cals, 4 Checks, 10 g fat to the finished dish.

sausages with cannellini beans

SERVES **two** | 240 10 7

Prep: **5** minutes Cook: **40** minutes

A cheap and cheerful one-pot supper, which will warm you up on a cold evening. You can use cannellini, haricot or butter beans – it makes no difference.

4 low-fat sausages

spray oil

1 large onion, thinly sliced

2 carrots, chopped

2 garlic cloves, crushed

1 x 400 g/14 oz can cannellini or other beans, rinsed and drained

1 x 200 g/7 oz can chopped Italian tomatoes

100 ml/3½ fl oz hot stock

1 tablespoon tomato purée

salt and ground black pepper

2 tablespoons chopped parsley

1 Place a flameproof casserole sprayed with oil over a medium heat. Add the sausages and brown all over. Remove.

2 Add the onion, carrots and garlic to the casserole and cook for at least 5 minutes, until softened. Stir in the beans, tomatoes, hot stock and tomato purée. Heat through and add the sausages. Season with salt and pepper.

3 Cook, uncovered, in a preheated oven at 200°C, 400°F, Gas Mark 6 for 20–25 minutes. Serve sprinkled with parsley.

OR...

You can use vegetarian or Quorn sausages instead.

roast chicken tray bake

SERVES **two** | 250 10 16

Prep: **5** minutes Cook: **45** minutes

The beauty of this meal is that everything is cooked in the same roasting pan which reduces the washing up! A great dish for a cold day in January.

2 chicken drumsticks and 2 thighs

2 red onions, peeled and quartered

2 yellow peppers, de-seeded and cut into chunks

1 small squash, de-seeded and quartered

1 lemon cut into wedges

6 unpeeled garlic cloves

few sprigs of fresh thyme and rosemary

spray olive oil

juice of 1 lemon

salt and ground black pepper

1 Put the chicken, onions, peppers, squash and lemon quarters in a roasting pan. Tuck in the unpeeled garlic cloves and herb sprigs, and spray lightly with olive oil.

2 Sprinkle with lemon juice and salt and pepper. Bake in a preheated oven at 200°C, 400°F, Gas Mark 6 for 45 minutes. Halfway through, turn the chicken and vegetables in the pan.

3 Transfer the chicken and vegetables to 2 serving plates. Discard the herbs. Squeeze the garlic pulp out of their skins over the vegetables. Eat with red or green cabbage.

OR...

You can remove the chicken skin before cooking; if so, one serving will be only 150 cals, 6 Checks, 6 g fat – a big saving!

winter dhal with sweet potato

SERVES **two** | 360 **14** ①

Prep: **5** minutes Cook: **40** minutes

You don't have to be a vegetarian to enjoy this warming spicy dish. This is real comfort food in the dark mid winter season.

1 onion, chopped
2 garlic cloves, crushed
knob of fresh root ginger, peeled and chopped
1 tablespoon curry paste
1 large sweet potato, cubed
seeds of 3 cardamom pods
1 teaspoon cumin seeds
115 g/4 oz split red lentils
½ teaspoon turmeric
350 ml/12 fl oz vegetable stock
salt and ground black pepper
3 tablespoons roughly chopped coriander
2 tablespoons low-fat yoghurt

1 Cook the onion, garlic, ginger and curry paste in a large saucepan over a low heat for 4–5 minutes, stirring. Add the sweet potato, cardamom and cumin seeds and continue cooking for 4–5 minutes.

2 Stir in the lentils with the turmeric and then add the hot stock. Bring to the boil, then cover the pan and simmer for about 25 minutes, or until the stock has been absorbed and the lentils are cooked.

3 Season with salt and pepper and stir in the coriander. Serve hot topped with a spoonful of yoghurt.

Italian caramelised oranges

SERVES **four** | 160 **6** ⓪

Prep: **15** minutes Chill: **2–3** hours Cook: **10** minutes

The best oranges to use for this refreshing dessert are seedless ones if you can buy them. Prepared in this way, the oranges look and taste sensational.

4 large juicy seedless oranges
100 g/3½ oz granulated sugar
100 ml/3½ fl oz water
juice of 1 orange

1 Thinly pare the peel from 2 oranges and cut into thin strips. Cook in a small pan of boiling water for 5 minutes, until softened. Pour through a sieve and leave to drain.

2 Remove all the pith and peel from the oranges. Place them in a dish and sprinkle the drained peel strips over the top.

3 Put the sugar, water and orange juice in a pan and cook over low heat, stirring until the sugar dissolves. Turn up the heat and boil until the syrup is reduced and just starting to caramelise. Watch it carefully – don't let it burn.

4 Pour the syrup over the oranges and refrigerate for a few hours. Serve the oranges whole or cut horizontally into thin slices, secured in shape with a cocktail stick.

SERVES **two** 305 **12** Ⓣ smoked haddock omelette

Prep: **5** minutes Cook: **15** minutes

This is a low-calorie take on a traditional English dish. You can used the dyed yellow smoked haddock fillets or natural smoked finnan haddock, which is a tawny colour.

225 g/8 oz smoked haddock fillets
5 medium eggs
2 tablespoons snipped chives
spray oil
salt and ground black pepper
1 tablespoon grated Parmesan cheese

1 Put the haddock in a shallow pan covered with water. Cover and simmer gently for 5 minutes, until cooked and opaque. Remove the haddock, peel away any skin and pick it over for bones. Break the flesh into large pieces and set aside.

2 Beat the eggs with a tablespoon of water, the chives and some salt and pepper.

3 Lightly spray a non-stick frying pan with oil and place over a medium heat. Pour the omelette mixture into the hot pan. When it starts to set around the outside, draw it into the middle and tilt the pan so the uncooked egg runs to the sides. When it is set underneath but still moist on top, scatter the smoked haddock over it and sprinkle with Parmesan.

4 Pop the pan under a hot grill for 2–3 minutes to brown the top. Serve in wedges with courgettes and cherry tomatoes.

SERVES **four** 70 **3** ① Tuscan soup

Prep: **15** minutes Cook: **1¼** hours

This may be traditional Italian peasant food but it's also warming and nutritious and is a meal in itself. Use the seasonal dark green cabbage, Savoy or January King in this substantial soup.

1 large onion, chopped
2 celery sticks, chopped
1 leek, chopped
2 large carrots, diced
2 garlic cloves, crushed
2 bay leaves
2 sprigs of fresh sage
1200 ml/2 pints vegetable stock
225 g/8 oz ripe tomatoes, skinned and quartered
1 x 400 g/14 oz can cannellini beans, rinsed and drained
225 g/8 oz shredded cabbage
salt and ground black pepper
small bunch of parsley, chopped

1 Put the onion, celery, leek, carrots, garlic, bay leaves, sage and stock in a large saucepan and bring to the boil.

2 Add the tomatoes and simmer gently for 45 minutes. Add the beans and cabbage, season to taste, and then cook for 10–15 minutes, until the cabbage is cooked and tender.

3 Check the seasoning and stir in the parsley. Remove the bay leaves and sage and serve piping hot.

OR...

For a more filling soup, add 60 g/2 oz small soup pasta with the cabbage. This will add 50 cals, 2 Checks per person.

deluxe cheese and potato pie

SERVES **two** | 305 | **12** | **8**

Prep: **15** minutes Cook: **30–40** minutes

Don't be put off by the name of this dish – it bears no resemblance to the stodge you were served up for school dinners! This is the gourmet slimming version par excellence!

450 g/1 lb potatoes

3 tablespoons very low-fat natural yoghurt

2 tablespoons skimmed milk

85 g/3 oz half-fat Cheddar cheese, grated

1 onion, finely chopped

1 leek, trimmed and sliced into rounds

spray oil

115 g/4 oz button mushrooms, sliced

4 ripe tomatoes, skinned and quartered

1 tablespoon chopped parsley

salt and ground black pepper

1 Peel the potatoes and cut them into large chunks. Place in a large saucepan and cover with salted water. Bring to the boil and cook for 15–20 minutes, until cooked and tender. Don't overcook them – they should not be mushy.

2 Drain the potatoes thoroughly, then tip them back into the warm pan and mash them with the yoghurt and milk. Beat well with a whisk or wooden spoon until they are fluffy. Season to taste with salt and lots of black pepper, and then stir in two-thirds of the grated cheese.

3 While the potatoes are cooking, cook the onion and leek in the spray oil in a hot shallow pan. When they soften, add the mushrooms and continue cooking until browned. Stir in the tomatoes and cook for 2–3 minutes. Season with salt and pepper and stir in the parsley.

4 Spoon half the potato mixture into a deep ovenproof dish. Smooth the surface and pour the onion and mushroom mixture over the top. Cover with the remaining mashed potato, then rough up the surface with a fork and sprinkle with the rest of the grated cheese.

5 Cook in a preheated oven at 180°C, 350°F, Gas Mark 4 for 15–20 minutes until heated right through and crisp and golden brown on top. Eat piping hot with salad or green vegetables.

OR...

You can vary the flavours of this dish by substituting some mashed parsnips or swede for some of the potato. Other vegetables can be added to the filling layer, depending on what you have available and what's in season. Try colourful red, green or yellow peppers, or chunks of courgette.

black bean chilli con carne

SERVES **two** 230 9 7

Prep: **5** minutes Cook: **30** minutes

Instead of a traditional bowl of chilli made with red kidney beans, try this quick version using canned black beans, which are now available in many supermarkets. Serve with salsa and crisp salad leaves.

1 onion, finely chopped
225 g/8 oz minced beef (max. 5% fat)
1 small red pepper, de-seeded and chopped
1 garlic clove, crushed
1 red chilli, de-seeded and finely chopped
1 x 400 g/14 oz can chopped tomatoes
1 teaspoon tomato purée
1 x 200 g/7 oz can black beans or other beans, rinsed and drained
salt and ground black pepper
1 tablespoon chopped fresh coriander
2 tablespoons tomato salsa
2 tablespoons virtually fat-free fromage frais

1 Dry-fry the onion and minced beef in a shallow pan over a medium heat. Add the red pepper, garlic and chilli and cook for 2–3 minutes.

2 Add the chopped tomatoes, tomato purée and beans, and increase the heat. When it starts to boil, reduce to a simmer and cook for 20 minutes. Season with salt and pepper. If the sauce thickens too much, thin it with water or beef stock.

3 Serve sprinkled with coriander on a bed of plain boiled rice (100 cals, 4 Checks, 0.5 g fat for each 30 g/1 oz dry weight or 75 g/2½ oz cooked weight) with the salsa and fromage frais.

OR...

Instead of a fresh chilli, you could use some hot chilli powder or dried chilli flakes.

orange chicken with rice

SERVES **two** 390 16 3

Prep: **5** minutes Cook: **35** minutes

Another easy supper dish for when you dash in from work and want to collapse in front of the television. Here the natural sweetness of the orange juice is offset by the zesty marmalade.

2 tablespoons natural low-fat yoghurt
60 ml/2 fl oz fresh orange juice
1 teaspoon Dijon mustard
4 teaspoons thin-cut marmalade
2 x 150 g/5 oz skinless, boneless chicken breasts
85 ml/3 fl oz chicken stock
salt and ground black pepper
100 g/3½ oz basmati rice
1 tablespoon chopped parsley

1 Mix the yoghurt, orange juice, mustard and marmalade. Use to coat the chicken breasts and place in a small roasting pan.

2 Bake in a preheated oven at 200°C, 400°F, Gas Mark 6 for 20 minutes. Remove from the oven and stir the stock into the pan juices. Season with salt and pepper.

3 Continue baking in the oven for a further 10–15 minutes until the chicken is thoroughly cooked. Meanwhile, cook the rice according to the packet instructions.

4 Divide the cooked rice between 2 serving plates, place a chicken breast on top, pour over the pan juices and sprinkle with parsley. Serve with salad or green vegetables.

pancakes with chocolate sauce

SERVES **four** 270 **11** ⑥

Prep: **10** minutes Stand: **10** minutes Cook: **10** minutes

115 g/4 oz plain flour
pinch of salt
1 large egg
300 ml/½ pint skimmed milk
spray oil
4 level scoops low-fat vanilla
ice cream

Chocolate sauce:
30 g/1 oz plain chocolate, grated
1 tablespoon unsweetened cocoa
powder
150 ml/¼ pint skimmed milk
1 tablespoon cornflour
artificial sweetener, to taste

1 Make the pancake batter: sift the flour and salt into a bowl and whisk in the egg and milk until the batter is smooth and free from lumps. Set aside to stand for at least 10 minutes.

2 Lightly spray a small non-stick frying pan or omelette pan with oil and place over a medium heat. When it's really hot, pour in a little of the batter and tilt the pan so that it covers the base. When the pancake is set and golden underneath, flip it over and cook the other side. Remove and keep warm while you cook the other pancakes – 8 in total.

3 Put the chocolate, cocoa, milk and cornflour in a small pan and heat gently, whisking all the time, until the sauce thickens and is smooth. Sweeten with artificial sweetener.

4 Divide the ice cream between the pancakes and fold them over. Put 2 on each serving plate and quickly pour over the chocolate sauce. Eat immediately.

OR...

If you prefer a more traditional approach, just sprinkle each pancake with ½ teaspoon caster sugar and then be generous with freshly squeezed lemon juice (85 cals, 3.5 Checks, 1 g fat per pancake). Orange juice makes another citrusy alternative.

Pancake Day usually falls in February, and if you don't want the usual pancakes with lemon, why not try this version with a yummy chocolate sauce?